MR. BADGER AND MRS. FOX #3

WHAT A TEAM!

Brigitte **LUCIANI** & Eve **THARLET**

Graphic Universe™ • Minneapolis • New York • London

For Christian, Brigitte, Marguerite, and Edmond
for the escape they gave me...
—E.T.

Story by Brigitte Luciani

Art by Eve Tharlet

Translation by Edward Gauvin

First American edition published in 2011 by Graphic Universe™.
Published by arrangement with MEDIATOON LICENSING – France.

Monsieur Blaireau et Madame Renarde
3/Quelle équipe!
© DARGAUD 2009 – Tharlet & Luciani
www.dargaud.com

Graphic Universe™
A division of Lerner Publishing Group, Inc.
241 First Avenue North
Minneapolis, MN 55401 U.S.A.

Website address: www.lernerbooks.com

Library of Congress Cataloging-in-Publication Data available.

ISBN: 978-0-7613-5627-1

Manufactured in the United States of America
3 - 45371 - 11241 - 3/12/2019

Are you OK?

I'm terrific!

Your turn now!

Do I have to do a flip?

No!
We all do what we want.

OK,
but whoever has the best jump wins!

5

Ginger!

You're disturbing a team of great athletes!

Great athletes? You're the biggest lazybones ever, almost brothers!

C'mon, lazy boys!

Why does she call them her "almost brothers"?

Because they've been living as brothers and sister ever since Mr. Badger and Mrs. Fox moved in together.

What now, athletes?

Take a jump! Then you won't be so snooty.

What are you doing?

Watch, Berry! You poke and you pull.

We're making a snail salad.

I'm showing Berry how to take off the shells.

Oho!

You take them off?

Of course! It's a lot easier to chew without the shell.

I like crunching them with my teeth.

I'd lose my appetite!

Not me. On the contrary, it adds a delicious walnut taste.

crunch!

Berry, I think we'll make them…

…half with shells and half without shells.

Injer!

Hi-hi! We just dropped in for some tools.

Whatever for?

We're going to make a boat.

booaaat!

A boat?

That's another one of Bristle's big ideas, isn't it?

Uh…

No.

Booaaat!

No, sweetie. You can't go with them.

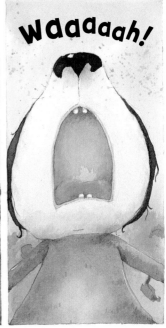

Waaaaah!

Waaaaah!

Sorry, but the river is much too dangerous for you.

Too bad she can't swim yet.

Waaaaah!

I think I have a solution.

Now you can float. You're lucky you have such smart brothers, Berry!

Bristle has incredible ideas, and Grub's great at making things.

We're the best team in the world!

Now hurry down to the river, or the others will build a boat without you.

So what? Big deal.

Oh really?

BOoaaat!

We'll get in more arguments than get work done, anyway.

Says you!

A sailboat? That's stupid!

Why is that stupid?

The river is too narrow. You won't be able to steer.

If the wind blows the opposite way, your sail will slow down the boat.

Really! Use your head!

Then what should we do?

Oh, that's easy...

I've had it, Bristle!

Grub?

Crrrack

Finally!
No time to
waste.

Look!
I drew a plan for
our boat.

Your
boat, you
mean.

Why?
Aren't you on
my team?

You're the one
who won't be on
the same team as
everyone else!

I just want to have some fun. I'm tired of your contests!

I'm sticking with everyone else.

You do what you want.

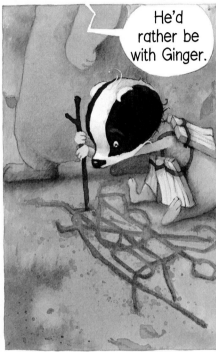

He'd rather be with Ginger.

Injer!

First, she steals my friends, and then she steals my own brother!

Injer!

I hate her!

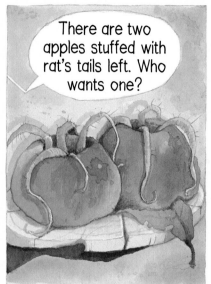

There are two apples stuffed with rat's tails left. Who wants one?

Not you, Bristle? What's the matter?

I'm not hungry.

That's no surprise. You ate the snails **and** the shells.

You don't know what good food is!

Well, two apples for three mouths. How should I divide these?

Ask Bristle!

He always has the best ideas!

Cut each apple in three pieces, and then give each person one piece of each apple.

Bravo! Good answer!

Niiice!

No... seriously!

You mean the three boats.

How is the boat going?

'Cause these two clowns each have to build their own boat!

Really?
You're making
your sailboat all
by yourself?

I have to
now! Or else when
you win, you'll say,
"I told you so."

So...you're
not working
together?

Nope!
I'm working with our
otter and weasel
friends.

Marguerite?
I guess I **would**
like some apple,
please!

Oh!
All gone!

DONG DONG **DONG!**

DONG!

Hurry up!

Boat race time!

Contestant #1 is the raft of the "Friends" Team!

Start

Contestant #2 is Ginger's catamaran.

And contestant #3 is Bristle with his kayak.

Get ready!

Three…

Two…

One…

Go!

Bristle is the first one off...

Bye-bye, guys!

Ginger seems to be having a little problem...

Followed by the raft of the Friends!

Start

Hey, watch it! Where's the fire?

But now she's off! The race is on for contestant #2!

27

I stink!

I have good ideas and I can make great plans...

...but I can't do anything all alone!

But all of you did pretty well without me!

I had help.

And I ended up just like you! In the water!

You made a great boat!

I was wrong. That sail was a great idea!

Are you kidding?

No... seriously!

You just need a way to let the sail down when there's a big gust of wind.

Hmm... I think I know a way!

Oh no! Here we go again!

You just need a rope on the sail, and...

It was just an idea...

Go on, tell us how!

We'll only do it if you want to.

Because to win, I need **all of you!**

What a team!

You said it!